To Judi + Luca —

Brian Bogart
2016

Captain PERSEVERANCE
How I Became a Superhero

By Brod Bagert
Pictures by Cam Aitkenhead

I'm a real-life superhero,
and I started out LIKE YOU.

But now I ***LOVE*** to read as much as eating chocolate cake.

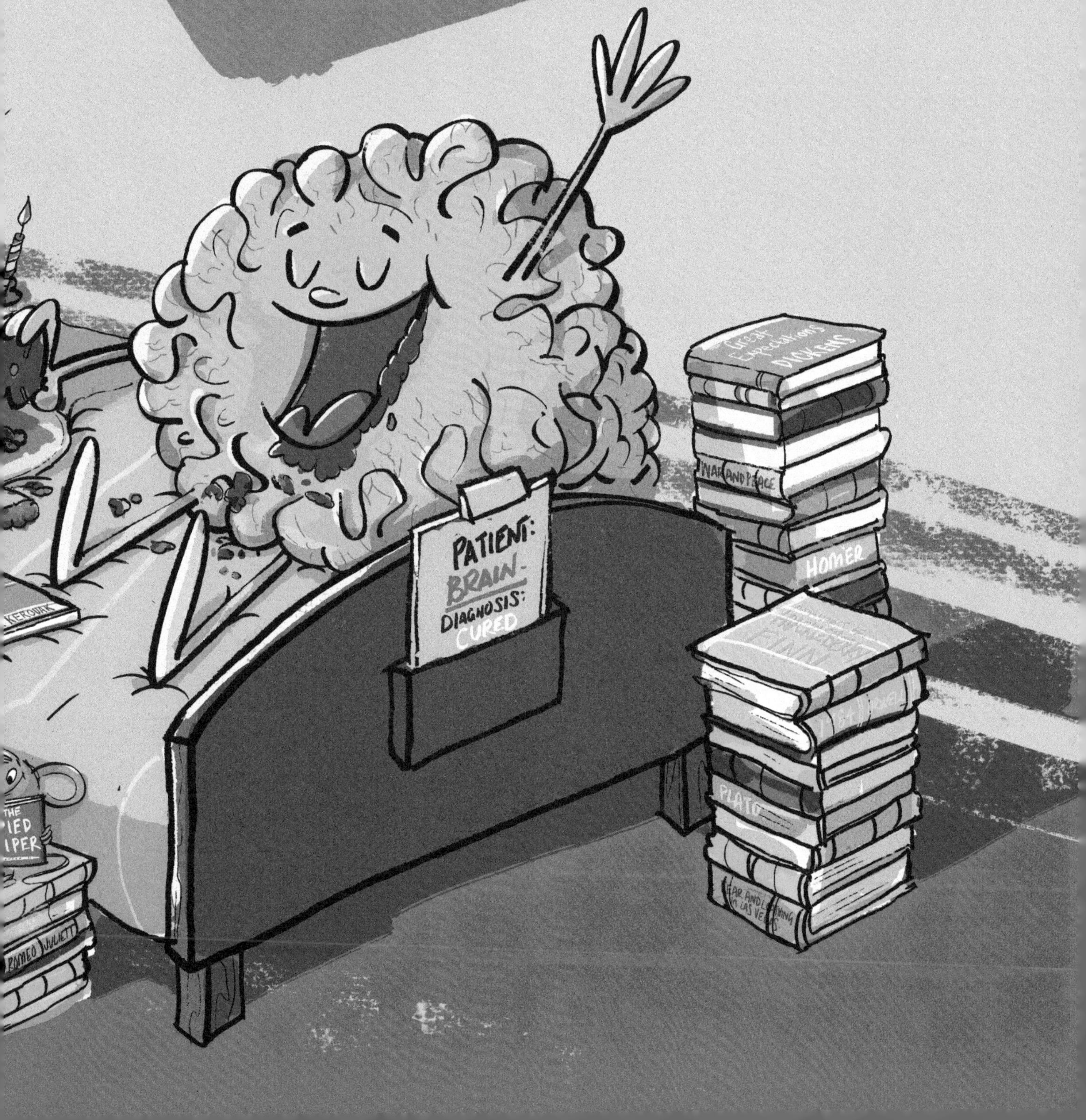

And fourth grade long division, it gave me such a **FRIGHT.**

In fifth grade it was science fair,
I almost threw a fit.
For **THREE WHOLE MONTHS** I struggled...

And trying out for sixth grade band was not a lot of fun.
But after two long years of WORK...

So why is all this happening?
I think it's pretty clear.
You're looking at a person
who has learned to PERSEVERE.

Brod Bagert is the award-winning author of 17 books of poetry for children, young-adults, and adults. His work has received numerous awards including the International Literacy Association's prestigious Young Adults Choices award, the Association of Educational Publishers Distinguished Achievement Award, the Independent Publisher Gold Book Award, and Mom's Choices Gold Medal.

Born and raised in the City of New Orleans, Brod studied the classics in Latin and Greek, wrestled and boxed to vent adolescent angst, fell in love with and married his high-school sweetheart, practiced law, served in public office, and reared four children that are the joy of his life.

Today Brod mesmerizes audiences with poetry, both his and those of the great authors of history, leaving participants with a new or reinvigorated love for poetry in the process.

Cam Aitkenhead is an illustrator from Perth, Western Australia. He has been coloring things in since he can remember and continues to do so in a professional capacity for a range of projects including children's books, editorials and animations.

His formal educational background was in architecture, graduating with a Bachelor's Degree in Environmental Design from the University of Western Australia in 2001. However, after working in the industry for about 10 years, Cam decided it was all a bit serious and perhaps children's books might be a LOT more fun to work on...turns out it was true! In addition to illustrating them, Cam also works on animating children's stories for apps and digital content.

He has lived and worked in Canada and the USA, a currently resides in Perth, Western Australia with his wife Claire, and son James.

Dedications

To My magnificent grandson Hawkins
-B.B.

His wonderful new son James, and his beautiful wife Claire.
-C.A.

Publishing Information

Published by Juliahouse Publishing
PO Box 792330
New Orleans, LA 70179
United States of America

Library of Congress Catalog Card No. 2016930858

Hardcover ISBN 978-0-9964665-4-7
Paperback ISBN 978-0-9964665-5-4
eISBN 978-0-9964665-6-1

1. Schools—Juvenile poetry. 2. Education—Juvenile poetry. 3. Children's poetry, American.

Acknowledgements and Thanks

Dr. Angela Duckworth, American psychologist and winner of the 2013 MacArthur Fellowship, for her work in the study of grit.

Dr. Jim Grant, founder of SDE (Staff Development for Educators, Inc.), for introducing me to the concept of grit and planting the seed for this book;

And my dad, who instilled in me the notion that perseverance was very nearly an end itself.

CPSIA information can be obtained
at www.ICGtesting.com
Printed in the USA
LVOW06*1926240316

480646LV00007B/9/P